Bob's Problem

by Margaret Adams

Bob's Problem
Text copyright © Margaret Adams 2009
Illustrations copyright © Ian Bobb 2009
Edited by Catherine White

First published and distributed in 2009 by Gatehouse Media Limited

Printed by Wallace Printers, Westhoughton

ISBN: 978-1-84231-056-4

British Library Cataloguing-in-Publication Data:
A catalogue record for this book is available from the British Library

Gatehouse Media Limited provides an opportunity for writers to express their thoughts and feelings on various aspects of their lives. The views expressed are not necessarily those of the publishers.

Author's Thanks

I would like to thank those people who struggle with alcohol or drugs and who have been brave enough to do something about it, a day at a time. It is thanks to them that *Bob's Problem* was written.

Chapter 1: Bob's job

Bob had worked in the supermarket for years.

He liked it there.

He worked with some very friendly people.

Not all of them were friendly,

but most of them were.

Bob's job was to work on the dairy counter.

Every morning he put out the milk.

He made sure there was enough butter,

enough cheese and plenty of yogurts

in the fridge.

It all needed to be ready for when

the customers wanted to buy it.

Working on the dairy counter

was the nearest that Bob would get

to his dream.

He loved animals and would have loved

to work on a farm.

The nearest he got to a cow

was putting milk in the fridge!

Never mind.

He did like his job.

There were a lot worse things he could do.

Bob was thinking about this one morning
when he was putting out the milk.
He always got to work very early.
There were not many people there yet
and he enjoyed the quiet.

It was a lovely day
and he had enjoyed the walk to work.
He was thinking he was lucky
to have the best job in the supermarket.
There were other jobs
that he would not have wanted.
He had just put out the last of the cheese
when the boss came over to him.

"Bob," he said,
"I want to give you a different job.
Come to my office so we can talk about it."

Chapter 2: The worst possible job

Bob went over to the manager's office
with the boss.
He was a bit sad.
He liked working on the dairy counter.
He did not really want to change jobs -
unless they were opening a farm
and that did not seem likely!

"Bob," said the boss,
"you have been working on the dairy counter
for a long time.
It is time you did other jobs.
I am going to put Jenny
on the dairy counter."

Bob was cross.
He knew the boss was seeing Jenny.

It did not seem fair that she was to get his job.

But what could he do?

The boss carried on talking.

"I want you to work on beers, wines and spirits.

You will put the cans and bottles out

for the customers.

It is heavy work -

too heavy for women,

but you will be fine."

Bob's heart sank.

There were other jobs in the supermarket

that he would not have minded.

But this was the one job he did not want.

He did not know what to do

or what to say.

Bob had never told anyone at work

about his problem.

Bob had not had a drink for five years.

He never went into pubs or clubs.

It was years since he had been to a party.

He stayed away from drink.

He needed to keep it that way.

He used to drink a lot.

His wife had left him.

He had lost his home.

He had not been able to keep a job.

But for five years,

he had not had a drink.

His life was better now.

His wife had not come back to him,

but he saw his children every week.

He had a nice little flat,

where he lived with his cat.

He had kept his job

at the supermarket too.

Every week, he went to meetings

to talk about it with people

who had the same problem.

But he had never told anyone at work.

He had never told his boss.

He had wanted to keep it a secret.

He did not know what to do.

Chapter 3: The truth

Bob knew that he had to tell his boss.
He would find it too difficult
putting out cans and bottles all day.
He would not risk it.
It was too hard for him.
He just hoped he could count on his boss
to understand.

It was about lunchtime
when Bob went up to the office
to speak to his boss.
He took the long way round to the office
so that he could put it off
for as long as possible.
He knocked on the door.
There was a sound from the other side
as the boss came to open it.

The boss had some money on the table.

He was counting the five pound notes.

There was a picture of a bloodhound

on the desk - the boss's dog.

It was taken outside the boss's house

on the south side of the city.

In the corner,

there was a mound of lost property

from the shop.

Bob looked at all of these things

because it took his mind off

what he had to say.

"What do you want, Bob?

I am very busy."

His boss sounded angry.

This was not a good start.

Bob coughed to clear his throat.

His voice sounded strange to him,

as though he was listening

to someone else speaking.

"I cannot do the job
on the drinks counter, boss.
I have a problem around drink.
I would like this to be kept
between the two of us.
I will do any other job you ask me."

His boss looked astounded.
He was proud that he knew
all about his staff.
But he did not know this.

"I will think about it, Bob," he said.

Chapter 4: The next day

Bob was proud of the way
he had spoken to his boss.
He felt sure he had done the right thing.
He went to work the next morning,
sure that everything would be all right.

When Bob arrived,
Jenny, the boss's girlfriend,
was talking to Mary,
who worked on the checkout.
They looked over at him
and he knew they were talking about him.

He went into the staff room
to hang up his coat.
Peter, the man who collected the trolleys,
was in there, along with Emma.

She worked in the shop.

They both stopped talking when Bob came in.

"Oh hello, Bob," said Emma quickly.

Too quickly, thought Bob.

What were they talking about?

Bob hung up his coat
and went towards the lift.
It would take him down to the shop.
Dan was waiting by the lift
and so was Lily, one of the cleaners.

He heard Dan say,
"I don't care what they are saying, Lily.
We all have secrets."
They stopped talking when they saw Bob
and Lily walked away.

Bob asked Dan what they had been
talking about.
Dan told him that Jenny had told Lily
about his drink problem.
Lily had told other people.
Most people knew now.

"Don't worry about it, Bob," said Dan.

Bob was very angry.

He had asked the boss not to tell anyone.

Suddenly he heard the boss behind him.

"Come into the office, Bob," he said.

Chapter 5: Shocks

"I have thought about what you told me,"
his boss said.
"I need to know
that the people who work here
can come in daily
and do the job I have asked them to do.
I need to have faith in them.
I do not claim to understand your problem,
but I must make it plain to you
that I expect you to do any job
I ask you to do.
I need you to do the drinks as your main job.
I will not ask you again.
You are paid to do the job I ask you to do
or you leave.
I will wait until the end of the day
to hear what you are going to do."

Bob walked away from the office,

feeling as though his life had been

poured down the drain.

It was pouring with rain and hail outside

and that matched his mood.

All the work he had done had been in vain.

He had to think about what to do now.

He walked at a snail's pace

back into the shop.

He needed to think.

He walked through the doors into the shop.

He could see Mary at the checkout.

She looked very pale.

She looked as if she was going to faint.

A tall man was standing in front of her.

He had his back to Bob.

Bob had done a training course

about health and safety with Mary.

He knew her well.

He was just going to walk over to her

to see if she needed any aid,

when the man turned around.

He was holding a gun.

"This is a raid," he shouted.

"Get down on the floor!"

Chapter 6: The raid

Bob was angry.

He was afraid too,

but he was very angry.

He was angry with his boss.

He was angry with Jenny.

He was angry with Lily.

He was angry that he had to choose.

He was very angry with the man with the gun.

Bob looked at Mary.

He could see that she was afraid.

Other people in the shop looked afraid too.

People were doing as the man said

and they were getting down on the floor.

Well, not me, Bob thought.

He had to choose again.

He was not going to let this man beat him.
Bob walked slowly towards the robber.

"Let her go, mate," he said.
"Put the gun down.
It's not worth it."

All of the time he was talking,
he walked closer to the man.
The man began to look afraid.
He pointed the gun at Bob.
Bob was even more angry now,
but he sounded calm.
The man was looking at Bob
and Bob moved closer.
Mary looked at Bob
and looked at the man.

She bit the man's arm,

just as Bob jumped towards him.

The gun went off.

The man ran.

Bob fell to the floor.

Chapter 7: Time to choose

Bob woke up in hospital.

A nurse was standing by his bed.

She smiled when she saw Bob was awake.

"You are a hero," she told him.

"Your picture is in the local paper.

Everyone says how brave you were."

Bob knew that he was not brave.

He had been very angry.

He had not been thinking clearly,

or he would not have walked towards

a man with a gun.

He had been so angry that he had wanted

to get the gun off the man

and hit him with it.

Then he would have liked

to make his boss afraid,

just as he had felt afraid.

But that was not the right thing to do.

He knew that.

Now he knew what he had to do -

the right thing to do.

He was going to write a letter to Head Office

to complain that his boss had not kept

his secret.

He was going to complain

that he had not been treated fairly.

They would have to listen

if they thought he was a hero.

The doctor told Bob that he needed

to take some time off work.

It was too soon to go back.

Bob thought he would use the time
to look for another job.
He was not going to go back
to the supermarket.
He knew that.

"You have visitors," said the nurse.

His ex-wife and his children had come
to see him.
He told his ex-wife
what had happened at work
and what he was going to do.

"There is a job going at the City Farm,"
she told him.
"You could try that."

So he did.

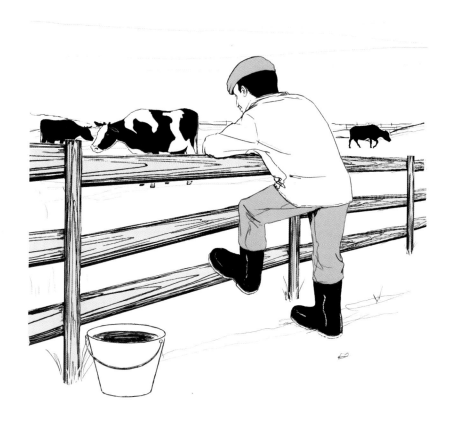

THE END

A comprehensive set of tutor resources, mapped
to the Adult Literacy Core Curriculum, is available
to support this book:

Bob's Problem Tutor Resources CD-Rom
ISBN: 978-1-84231-057-1

Coming soon in the Supermarket Stories series:

Dan's Dinner
ISBN: 978-1-84231-064-9

Dan's Dinner Tutor Resources CD-Rom
ISBN: 978-1-84231-065-6

Author's Note

I have written short stories for individual students on quite a few different occasions, usually to help them practise a particular letter pattern, consonant blend, digraph etc., or to meet an observed need of the particular student.

Bob's Problem is the second title in the Supermarket Stories series. It was initially written for an individual student who is himself in recovery from addiction.

The main intention of the series is to give entry level students a story to read. I have found that many books for students at this level don't have a story as such and, as someone who enjoys stories, I wanted to give my students the same opportunity. I wanted to show that reading can be a pleasure, not just a necessity.

They are stories for adults with adult themes. I have written them so that students can read one chapter per session and I have finished each chapter at a point that will encourage the reader to come back for more.

Each chapter can be used to practise specific learning aims, although this does not have to be the case. The supporting resources also check comprehension and encourage the reader to think more broadly about the text. I hope that this will encourage the reader to see the relevance of reading stories - they make you **think**, not just read.

Margaret Adams

If you have enjoyed this book, why not try one of these other titles from Gatehouse Books?

Pam's Secret   ISBN: 978-1-84231-050-2
by Margaret Adams

The first title in the Supermarket Series. Pam shares a secret with Jenny, her new friend at work. Will Jenny betray Pam's trust?

Life On The Buses   ISBN: 978-1-84231-025-0
by Eric Newsham

'Life on the buses. What fun! The best job I ever had in my life.' Read about some of the fun and antics Eric gets up to with his driver mate.

Getting Better   ISBN: 978-1-84231-026-7
by Marie McNamara

Marie's desire to improve herself is driven by the desperate wish to give her children a better start in life. *Getting Better* is an inspiring read.

Mudlake   ISBN: 978-1-84231-027-4
by B L Hinde

A ghostly story of mystery and intrigue. Was it an accident, or was it murder? You decide. A phonic adult beginner reader, focusing on the long vowel sounds.

Gatehouse Books®

Gatehouse Books are written for older teenagers and adults who are developing their basic reading and writing or English language skills.

The format of our books is clear and uncluttered. The language is familiar and the text is often line-broken, so that each line ends at a natural pause.

Gatehouse Books are widely used within Adult Basic Education throughout the English-speaking world. They are also a valuable resource within the Prison Education Service, the Probation Services, social services departments and secondary schools - both in basic skills and in ESOL teaching situations.

Catalogue available

Gatehouse Media Limited
PO Box 965
Warrington
WA4 9DE

Tel/Fax: 01925 267778
E-mail: info@gatehousebooks.com
Website: www.gatehousebooks.com